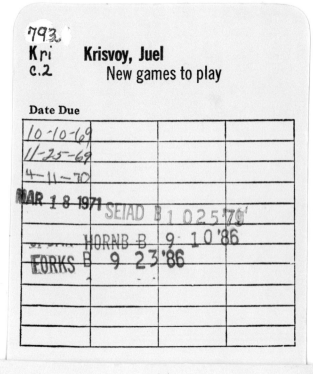

793

Kri
c.2

Krisvoy, Juel
New games to play

Date Due

10-10-69		
11-25-69		
4-11-70		
MAR 18 1971 SEIAD B 1 025 79		
HORNB B 9 10 '86		
FORKS B 9 23 '86		

More than sixty new children's games each of which includes a verse to chant while playing it.

New Games To Play

illustrated by
JERRY WARSHAW

NEW GAMES toPLAY

by Juel Krisvoy

FOLLETT PUBLISHING COMPANY

Chicago   New York

Library of Congress Catalog Card Number: 68-10491

First Printing

Follett Publishing Company
1010 West Washington Boulevard
Chicago, Illinois 60607

T/L   6162

In fond memory of my husband,
George Krisvoy

CONTENTS

NEW GAMES TO PLAY

★

Original games with chants
for children age three to six

COME PLAY WITH ME

Come out, come out, come play with me.
I see you hiding behind the tree.
Come out, come out, we'll have such fun.
Just catch me (name a child)**, but you'll have**
to run.

One child is chosen to be the caller. He stands out in the open, and the other children hide behind the tree (or any large object) and peek out.

The caller recites the above verse and names one child to run out and chase and tag him before he can reach the tree, where the others are hiding. If the caller is tagged, the child who tagged him may be the new caller. Otherwise, the original caller may have another turn until someone can tag him and take his place.

11

My Clown, Geewilliwillikins

I had a funny purple clown,
Who smiled at me when I would frown.
He did so many silly things.
Just watch Geewilliwillikins.

One child is chosen to be Geewilliwillikins. The others stand opposite him in a straight row. Now all speak the little verse together.

Then all must copy the funny antics of Geewilliwillikins. He will try to fool the children. Whoever is fooled and doesn't copy Geewilliwillikins correctly is out of the game. The last child who follows the antics correctly becomes the new Geewilliwillikins.

Examples of antics to try: twirl around; jump up and down; put one foot out, then the other; clap hands; stamp feet, and whatever tricks an imaginative child can think of.

The children are sleeping right over there.
Then out of a cave crawls a big black bear.
"What's going on?" He hears a noise.
He's coming to steal from the girls and
    boys.

The children have been shown a group of about ten objects on a picnic cloth laid on the floor, which represents the grass. Then all must turn their backs and cover their eyes. Now the children recite the verse above.

The child who is chosen to be the bear takes some of the objects and returns to his cave. Now all the children may look at the picnic cloth again. The child who is first to remember which objects are missing and is able to name them correctly may be the next bear. Use different objects each time the game is repeated.

13

TWIRLY, Whirly BALLOONS

Around and 'round I twirl through space,
My twirly balloon and I.
The stars all twinkle in my face,
While flying through the sky.

The children sit in a row on chairs. The chairs represent the earth. The children all stand up and twirl around and around while reciting the verse above. They twirl as far as they can across the yard or room in their imaginary balloons. Wherever each child falls over, having lost his balance, is where he must sit on a make-believe star. The one who wins the game is the child who twirls the greatest distance to a make-believe star.

The verse below is then spoken with the name of the winner.

Here we sit upon our stars,
As far as we could go.
(Name of child) **picked the highest star.**
We are down below.

14

My Lollipop Tree

Children on their knees form a circle.

I planted a little lollipop
And hoped to have a tree.

> The children place a closed fist in their laps. This is
> the lollipop seed. Then children put their closed fist
> on the floor in front of them and pat it down with
> the other hand, to plant it.

A tree just filled with lollipops.
For all my friends to see.

> Closed fists gradually rise as tree grows tall.
> Children reach as high as they can.

One day a bright red lollipop,
Popped up with two green leaves.

> One finger of their closed fist pops up.

Branches and leaves and lollipops,
Grew beyond the eaves.

> Then all fingers pop out.

16

One child is chosen to pretend to have given away all of his lollipops. Now he would like to have another child's lollipop. Verse below is repeated as he skips around the outside of the circle of children. He pretends to take a lollipop from the child whose name he calls. The child who has been called tries to catch him before he gets back to his place and eats all of his lollipops. If the child called catches him, he must try again some other place. He must skip around the circle and call someone's name, repeating the game as before.

I picked a basket of lollipops

For all my friends and me.

But I see prettier lollipops

On (name of a child) **lollipop tree.**

17

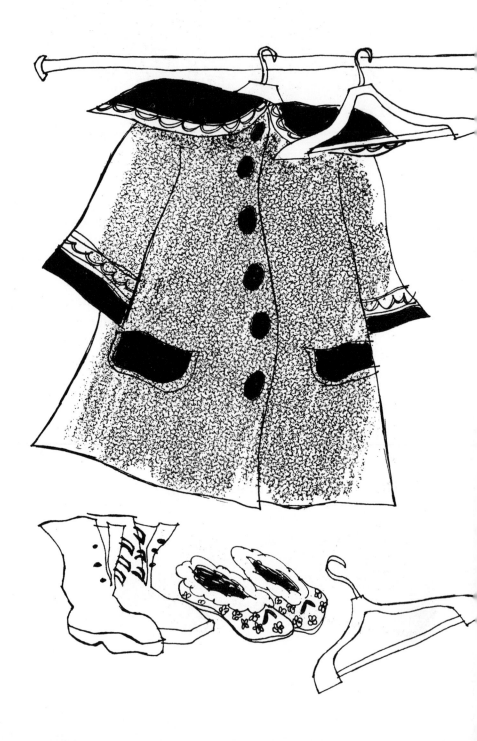

The Coat

**Please hang up your coat, when you come
through the door,
On a hanger you'll find for the coat that you
wore.**

Choose one child to be the mother or the father for this game. The other children leave the room and stand where they cannot see. The mother or father takes a wire coat hanger and hangs it someplace in the room. It must be hung where it can be seen, but not obviously so. It will be difficult to find the wire coat hanger, even when hung in plain sight, as a wire coat hanger blends into the surroundings.

The mother opens the door to let the children in, and she recites the verse. The children come in and search for the coat hanger. The first child to find the hanger in the room wins the game and becomes the new mother or father for the next game.

19

WHOSE LITTLE SHADOW, ARE YOU?

Each child has a partner for this game. One child plays the part of himself, and the other child is his shadow, who does whatever he does.

Whose little shadow are you?

Point at shadow.

I'll show you just what to do.

Point at self.

Now jump little shadow, so.

Both jump.

Then bend and touch your toe.

Bend and touch toe.

Now clap little shadow, stop.

Both clap hands and stop.

Then twirl like a whirling top.

Twirl around.

Sit down on the floor and no more!

Sit down and sigh.

Now let's run out the door!

Children hold the hands of their shadows and race to see which child and his shadow reach the door first.

The spoon stirs up the cake, yes,
Cup by cup.
Let's put in the (name of ingredient),
And stir it all up.

22

Choose one child to be the spoon. The other children form a circle around the spoon. They represent the mixing bowl.

The bowl now dances in a circle around the spoon and chants the verse. Each time it is repeated, the spoon chooses a different ingredient to mix into the cake. One child may be the flour, the others may be the sugar, the butter, the baking powder, the salt, milk, vanilla, eggs, etc.

The spoon twirls each one around as he is stirred into the cake batter. The ingredients remain in the center with the spoon.

When all the ingredients are chosen and stirred into the cake, they stoop down and pretend to bake in the oven. They slowly rise as the cake bakes. When they stand up straight, the cake is done.

The children on the outside, who form the bowl, try to grab a piece of the cake as it tries to escape and hide in the cupboard (some designated hiding place) for a party. The first child to grab a piece of cake may be the new spoon in the next game.

A simpler version may be played, if just a small number of children are present. The spoon may mix up a cake mix without a bowl. He may choose three ingredients: the mix, eggs, and milk. He may give each of these ingredients a twirl around.

Two Little Bunnies

See the little bunnies,
Sleep beneath the tree.
> *Shhhhh!*

Children place two closed fists in their laps to represent two bunnies.

Wake up you funny bunnies.
You're sleeping near a bee!
> *Bzzzzzzzz!*

Now children make the index fingers and middle fingers of each hand pop up. These fingers are the bunnies' ears.

Children sit in a circle. The leader whispers in each child's ear. Secretly, she appoints one child to be the bee. The others don't know who it is.

Now everyone says the verse and acts out the above directions. On the word *"Bzzzzzzzz,"* the appointed bee jumps up and stings or touches as many children as he can before they can reach the tree safely. Designate a spot in the distance to represent the tree.

Choose different children to be the bee. Then see which bee is able to sting the most children.

24

THE HOUSE WITH A WALL

Around the house, we're building a wall,
Ten feet tall, we won't let it fall.

The children line up in a long row and walk slowly past a pile of toy bricks which have been previously laid on the floor. Each child picks up one brick and proceeds to a designated spot nearby. This spot is where the children will attempt to build their wall, one brick at a time.

The first brick is laid down by the first child in the line, and the next child lays his brick right on top of the first brick. Each child in the row repeats the action. All the bricks must be piled carefully on top of the original brick, building the pile straight up with no bricks at the side.

The purpose of the game is to see who lasts the longest without knocking down any bricks. Whoever knocks down or drops a brick is eliminated from the game. The children continuously pile up one brick at a time and then return for another brick, if their brick has not fallen. The children must stay in line throughout the game except to step out to put on their bricks or to step out and away from the game if they have been eliminated for knocking down any bricks. Blocks may be used for bricks.

27

The LITTLE CLOUDS

In this game, the children are little clouds who must travel to the moon before it is dark. One child sits in a far corner to represent the moon. Another child is chosen to be a big black rain cloud. The cloud stands along the route of travel. Still another child, standing a little beyond, represents the flash of lightning. The remaining children are the clouds, all traveling slowly as the verse below is recited.

Each cloud must follow the directions given with the verse, as the leader acts it out. If any child fails to follow the leader's actions, he must go back to the beginning of the route of travel. The winners go to sleep and stay by the moon. The verse is spoken slowly.

Fluffy little clouds, all
Travel across the sky.

Children walk slowly with arms making a circle above their heads to represent a nice, round fluffy cloud.

Here's a big black rain cloud.
We must all keep dry.

Little clouds cover their heads with their hands and crouch way down.

Fluffy little clouds, all
Floating up and down.

Children stand on their toes, then bend way down.

Look, a flash of lightning.
The little clouds just frown.

They stop and put hands on hips and frown at the lightning as lightning child jumps out and claps hands to frighten the little clouds.

Fluffy little clouds, all
Hope to be there soon.

Clouds slowly continue along the route of travel, with arms arched over their heads as before until they reach the moon.

Hurry now, before it's dark.
We're sleeping by the moon.

Now the clouds all curl up and go to sleep.

29

Oh, tickle, tickle, tickle-bug, you can't tickle me.

I'll run and I'll hide in the old apple tree.

The children all stand still, scattered about the room. They recite the above verse. One child has been chosen to be the "tickle-bug," who goes about pretending he will tickle different children. When he really does tickle a child, this child must run to the old apple tree before he is tickled again. If he reaches the old apple tree, a spot designated by the leader, before he is tickled again, he becomes the new "tickle-bug."

If he is caught, however, he must remain by the old apple tree while the "tickle-bug" has another turn. No child in the game may move from his standing position unless he is actually tickled by the "tickle-bug."

30

**Bouncing and bouncing and bouncing the
ball,**
We can catch the ball when it hits the wall.

One child bounces a big beach-type ball on the ground near a wall. The other children speak the verse. They may try to catch the ball only when it is bounced against the wall while the verse is being recited.

The child who bounces the ball should not wait for the word "wall" to bounce the ball against the wall. He should bounce it against the wall at any time during the verse. This way it can be a surprise when it does hit the wall. The child who catches the ball when it hits the wall now has a chance to bounce the ball for the others to catch. The verse is repeated constantly during the game.

31

CHOOCHOO TRAIN

Choose one child to be the engine.

There was a little choochoo train,
Riding down the track.
Now stop you little choochoo.
A car hooks on your back.

32

Everyone recites the verse. The engine chugs along past the others. The engine chooses a child to hold onto his back. The children keep repeating the verse above, as one at a time another child is added to the rear of the train until it is completed with all the children. If a large group of children play, add two cars at a time. When all of the cars are attached, they are ready to go under the bridge.

The children chug along on an imaginary track. The leader holds up a stick to represent the bridges. Another child may help by holding the other end of the stick. The stick is lowered each time the train goes under it. Whoever is touched by the stick must leave the train and go back to the station, and must leave the game. The last one to remain untouched by the stick wins the game.

The verse below is repeated for passing under the bridges.

**Now we come to bridges, yes,
Some are very low.
If you can't go under them,
Back to the station you go.**

Come pick the fruit, we can't be late.
Then pile the fruit upon your plate.
The village people all await,
The fruit we bring to celebrate.

Five to ten children may play this game at one time. Each child is given a light aluminum pie plate. They pretend to be picking fruit in the jungle near their jungle village. They pile the fruit on their pie plates. Together, all of the children speak the verse. On the word "celebrate," the five children who have now lined up, each with a pie plate balanced on top of his head, walk toward a place designated to be the jungle village. Each time a pie plate falls off of any of their heads, they must stop and pick it up and place it on top of their heads again and continue walking. Whoever reaches the jungle village first wins in his group. Then the next group competes.

Finally, the winners from each group compete with each other in a last game. The final winner now stands in the center of all of the children as they beat on imaginary drums and dance in a circle around the winner to celebrate.

Valentine

For this game, the children all sit in a circle and recite the verse below.

She'll hide her little valentine.
Who will have her heart?
The one who guesses where it is
Must be quick and smart.

Choose a child to walk around the circle, holding a paper heart and speaking the verse below.

Hide it here, or hide it there?
Who knows where, oh who knows where?

This game may be played two ways.

For Older Children

Children sit in a circle, and the child who has been chosen to hold the paper heart skips around the inside of the circle pretending to place the heart into different hands, but actually leaving it secretly in one child's hands. The pretense continues a few moments, then the children are asked to guess who now has the heart. The child who guesses may hide the heart in the next game.

For Younger Children

The children sit in a circle, and the child who has been chosen to hold the heart for this game skips around the outside of the circle. Somewhere along the way, the child does leave the heart behind one child. As in the first version, the pretense continues for a few moments, then the children are asked to guess who now has the heart. The first child to guess who has the heart may hide the heart in the next game.

TIGER, TIGER

We came to catch a tiger.
Our mission cannot fail.
They said to catch you for our zoo,
To put salt upon your tail.

The children form a circle. One child is chosen to be the tiger. The tiger crawls about the circle on his hands and knees in the center of the circle. The leader pins a piece of cloth, a belt, or a sock on the back of the tiger where a tail would be. Then as the children and the leader chant the above verse, the leader walks around the circle behind the children and secretly taps two of them on the back.

When the verse ends, the two children who have been chosen run out and try to pull the tiger's tail before the tiger tags them. If the tiger tags them first, they are out of the game.

However, if a child is able to pull the tiger's tail first, he may be the new tiger. The former tiger must leave the game, as he has been captured. Each new tiger should try to stay in the game long enough to tag out all of the children. Then he may escape into the jungle and be free.

LITTLE INDIANS

Poor little Indians,
Don't know where to roam.
Little lost Indians,
Want to find a home.

Two Indian villages,
Which one shall it be?
We will take the best one.
Let's go down and see.

40

Two children are chosen to be the two Indian chiefs. Each of the two Indian chiefs has a drum to beat. Each of the chiefs sits near his tent. The tent is represented by two children facing each other and holding joined hands up to form an arch. Choose four children, two for each of the two chiefs' tents. The remaining children are the poor little lost Indians looking for a home. They stand at a distance and recite the verse.

The two chiefs beat on their drums as the lost Indians run whooping down the hill to the Indian tents.

First one Indian chief gives a war cry, and both children representing his tent close in and capture the Indians caught between them. The captives must stand behind the tent in which they were captured. Next the other Indian chief gives a war cry and his tent closes on the captives. The game continues with the Indian chiefs alternately giving war cries every few moments until all the little Indians are captured.

The game is ended with a tug-of-war with all the captives behind the chief who has captured them. The strongest chief and village win the game.

41

Sailing Home

Our little white boats sail over the foam. Here comes a big wind to blow us straight home.

All of the children sit in a row. Then the first five children step forward and stand side-by-side. They now pretend to be riding imaginary white sailboats. The children sway back and forth as they say, "Our little white boats sail over the foam. Here comes the big wind to blow us straight home." However, before the word "home" in the second line of the verse, the five children take a deep breath and say the word "home" as long as they can as they walk slowly toward a distant place that has been chosen to represent home. The children are competing to see who can say the word "home" on one breath, and walk the greatest distance at the same time. Each child stops where his breath runs out. Whoever lasts the longest in his group of five children is the winner.

Each new group of five children repeat the same procedure until all of the children have competed. The winners from each group of five children step forward, and the game is repeated for the last time to see who is the best sailor of them all.

No Zoo for This Kangaroo

"I won't be caught, but you can try.
No zoo for me," hop hop, "good-bye."

Let's catch a hopping kangaroo.
We'll put some in our favorite zoo.

This game is played with two teams. Team one starts the game as the kangaroo team. All of the kangaroos stoop down in a row in front of team number two. The children hold their hands like the kangaroo in the picture, and speak the first two lines. They hop to the safety rock which the leader has chosen at the start of the game.

Team two represents the zoo hunters on horseback. They, too, stoop low as if riding on their horses. They speak the last two lines and immediately start to chase the kangaroos. They must hop all of the way and try to tag as many kangaroos as possible before the kangaroos reach the safety rock. Now count the kangaroos caught by team number two.

Repeat the game, this time letting team number one be the hunters and team two the kangaroos.

Children of both teams must hop all of the time throughout the game, or they will be immediately disqualified.

45

I've come to save the princess,
A prisoner in her tower.
This magic crown will help me,
A crown of greatest power.

Choose one girl to be the princess in her tower. Choose a boy to be the prince. The prince speaks the verse above. The other children are enemy soldiers encircling the prince and princess. The prince has a magic crown with colored stones on it. Each colored stone produces a different magic power.

For example: the purple stone turns the soldiers into cows; the red into mice; the yellow into rabbits; the green into giants, and the blue into statues. The leader writes the magic powers of each stone on a piece of

46

paper. The prince does not know what power each stone has. He has only one chance to choose.

The prince starts the game by holding up his magic crown. This frees the princess from her tower. She joins the prince, but now they must both escape the encircling soldiers with the help of the magic crown.

The prince chooses a color and taps a colored stone, hoping to choose the color that will turn the soldiers to statues.

The prince says aloud, "I pick the (he names one of the colored stones)." The leader has the list telling what the magic power of each colored stone is. She tells the soldiers what the stone the prince has chosen makes them become. If they are mice or cows, they must crawl on their hands and knees; if they are rabbits, they must hop; if they are giants, they are lucky, as they can easily run after and try to capture the prince and princess before they are safe in the imaginary forest. If the soldiers are turned into statues, the prince and princess just walk away with no trouble at all, as the soldiers freeze right where they are—unable to move.

The crown can be made of paper with stones colored in crayon. Each time the game is played, mix up what the different colors represent. Originally the blue stone represented turning the soldiers into statues. For the next game, let the red stone turn them into statues, so each new prince will have difficulty guessing what the magic stones will do.

Here is my present, I'll give you a clue. Now guess what it is. Happy Birthday to you!

Choose three to five children to represent the birthday children at the party. The other children are the guests coming to the party. The guests each carry a little wooden block to represent the birthday presents. One child at a time steps up and recites the verse, then acts out what his birthday present is.

For example if his imaginary present is a dog, he barks. The gift could be a kitten, bird, ball, doll, train, or clock. The birthday guest may bring any kind of gift that he wishes. The birthday child who is the first to guess the birthday present being acted out receives the little wooden block that the guest is carrying. The next guest steps forward and repeats the same procedure. The birthday child with the most blocks becomes the winner after each guest has had his turn.

The HOPFLY BiRD

There was a strange bird, I'll tell you just why.

It had to hop high, before it could fly.

This game is a contest. A mark is taped on a wall or a chalk mark is made fairly high on the blackboard. The children line up and recite the verse. They are all hopfly birds having a contest to see who can hop and touch the high mark within three turns. The winners are the children who touch the high mark with the least number of turns.

The first group of winners then compete with each other to see who can become the very best hopfly bird. The tape mark is moved to a higher position, and the game is repeated until one child wins over all of the others. The winner over all is now the king or queen of the hopfly birds. All of the others line up behind their king or queen.

The Snail and the FROGS

The snail and the frogs went out to play.
The snail said, "Hooray, a frog race today!"
He told all the frogs, when to hop, hop, hop,
And when they should creep, and when they
should stop.

Choose one child to be the snail. The other children are the frogs and line up in a row for a frog race. All together the children recite the verse. Then the snail who is in charge begins the race.

The snail may tell the frogs to "hop" or "creep" or "stop" in any order or combination he wishes.

The object is to fool the frogs. The frogs must do as the snail tells them. Any frog who makes a mistake must leave the game. Whoever reaches the goal first without a mistake wins the frog race.

The Pirate and the Golden Key

Ahoy! You little pirates.
Who hides the golden key
To open a chest of treasures?
Surprises, you will see.

For this game all of the children are pirates. The leader secretly places between one and ten objects in a box. This box represents the treasure chest. After the box is filled, she puts it in the center of the floor. A pirate is chosen to stand in the center of the floor, next to the treasure chest. The pirate recites the verse.

The other children stand in a circle around him. One child has been given a little key. He passes it on. At the same time, all of the children pretend they are holding the key and passing it on from one to another. The pirate in the center must guess within a specified time who really does have the key.

If he guesses who is holding the key, he may have his turn to guess how many treasure objects he thinks are in the treasure chest. If he does not guess where the key is, he must "Walk the plank." (He walks in a straight line out of the game and sits down.)

Now another child is chosen to become the pirate, and the game is repeated. Repeat the game as often as you like, with a new pirate each time. The pirate who most closely guesses the number of objects in the chest is the winner of the treasures.

A Sailboat to Candy Island

Children stand in a row looking through a make-believe telescope. The telescope is made by making fists of their right and left hands: the right fist, thumb side toward the right eye, and the left fist placed against the right just touching the little finger of the right fist. Now the children make a slight opening in the two fists to peek through, and then chant the following verse.

Look, I see an island
Of wonderful things to eat.
Covered with candy and popcorn trees.
We're off in our sailboat fleet.

Children put their hands together above their heads to represent the sails of boats.

The leader recites the verse below. When she comes to the word go, everyone starts to sail toward a distant spot designated as Candy Island. The children must walk, not run. The teacher keeps repeating the words "Blow wind, blow," but often says "Stop." Any child who does not stop immediately on this word must go back to the starting line again. The first child to reach the island becomes the king or queen of the island. The others are the guests.

Each hopes to be the first one there,
But the wind must blow.
If it stops our sailboats stop,
And wait for a wind to go.
Blow Wind, Blow.

Sweep the house, oh, sweep it clean.
The cleanest house you have ever seen.

Choose two teams to play this game. The children say the above verse. Then two children, one from each team, hold a broom. If no broom is available, use a rolled up newspaper to represent the broom.

Now place a crumpled piece of paper in front of each child. The teams are at opposite ends of the room, and each child must sweep his paper to a spot in the center of the room.

Whoever gets to the center first wins the race for his team as the fastest and cleanest sweeper of his half of the house. The teams alternate until all the children have a turn. Then count which team has the most winners.

Knockity, knockity, knock, I say,
Who'll guess what I have in my basket today?

Choose six objects. Show the children, who are seated in a row, the six objects. One child is picked to be the salesman. The salesman is given a basket and a small cloth. He takes the six objects and leaves the room. The salesman returns to the room with only one of the objects in his basket to sell.

The salesman knocks on an imaginary door. The children say, "Come in." The salesman enters with his basket with the object he has chosen hidden from view. The first child to guess which object he is selling (all may guess, no turns are necessary) may be the next salesman. He may pick another object and the game is repeated as before.

59

PATTY, PATTY, PAT, PAT

Patty, patty, pat, pat, *shhh.*
Patty, patty, pat, pat, *shhh.*
Patty, patty, pat, pat, clap, clap, clap.

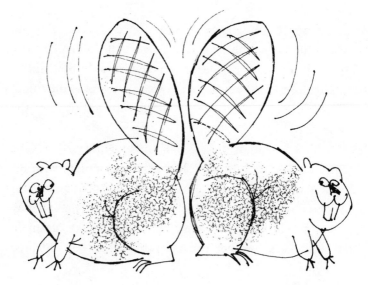

60

Choose one child to be the leader. The other children sit on chairs facing the leader. The children all follow the leader, reciting the verse as they pat out the rhythm of the patty, patty, pat, pat words on their thighs with their hands. On the word *shhh*, they put their index fingers to their lips. The children clap their hands on the words, clap, clap, clap. The leader then changes the words, clap, clap, clap, each time the verse is repeated. Use some of the examples below, or have the children create some of their own.

1. Jump up and down and say, "Jump, jump, jump."
2. Sit on the floor and say, "Sit, sit, sit."
3. Twirl around and say, "Twirl, twirl, twirl."
4. Children walk forward from their chairs as the leader says, "Walk, walk, walk."
5. Children stamp their feet at the command, "Stamp, stamp, stamp."

This game may be played at quite a fast pace in order to fool the children with the changes the leader makes to surprise them. The children who are fooled and do not follow the leader are eliminated. The youngsters take turns being the leader.

What will I take, oh, what will I pick?
Guess it, then catch me, Quickity-Quick.

The children all sit in a circle. One child is chosen to be Quickity-Quick. The leader shows all of the children three small objects. She then places the three objects behind three different children who are seated in the circle.

Quickity-Quick recites the verse above while walking behind the children. He pretends to take the different objects to fool the children, who must not look behind them. While he is pretending, he does actually take one object. Whenever one of the three children think their object has been taken, they immediately try to catch Quickity-Quick before he reaches a safety goal which has previously been established. If Quickity-Quick is caught with the object that was behind the child who chased him, they exchange places.

The game is then repeated with the new Quickity-Quick. However, if the child catches Quickity-Quick with an object that was not his object, he is disqualified. Quickity-Quick may try again. Also, if Quickity-Quick is not caught at all, he has another turn until he is caught.

63

BUZZING BUMBLEBEE

BUZZ · · · BUZZ · · · BUZZ · · · BUZZ

The flower children speak first.

Buzzing little bumblebee,
If I hide you won't find me.
Buzzing, buzzing, closer, closer.
Catch me, sting me, no sir, no sir!

The bumblebee then speaks.

"Who will I choose, which one will do?
I'll think and I'll think, and I think I'll choose
**   you!**
**   *Bzzz.*"**

Select one child to play the part of the bumblebee.
The other children are the flowers. They stand in a circle
and recite the first verse above.

Then the bumblebee recites his verse next and tries
to sting one of the flower children. The bumblebee may
only be allowed to sting a flower child who remains
standing. The flower children may only crouch down
when the bumblebee attempts to sting them. The flower
children who he stings before they can crouch down to
escape him must stay down. The last flower child standing, who has not been stung, becomes the new buzzing
bumblebee.

64

SPACE HOP

My rocket goes on a space hop, hop.
From planet to planet, we'll hop and stop.

66

This game may be played in two ways. Place some chairs (representing planets) about the room far apart from each other. The chair where the children start the game will represent the earth. All the children recite the verse as they begin to play the game.

1

The game starts on earth. One child at a time completes the trip. He hops on one foot, with as few hops as possible, from chair to chair (each chair represents a planet), resting a second at each planet. The child who has the least hops on his round trip to earth wins. All count the hops aloud, as each child separately has his turn. Write down the individual scores.

2

This second version is played with a larger group of children. All recite the verse above. Divide the children into teams of three to five. Each team has a separate turn in a hopping competition. Do not count the hops in this version. This is a race to see who can make the round trip on one foot and just touch each planet as he goes by without losing his balance. Those who fail must drop out. The winners from each team compete in the final race to see who is the winner of them all.

Our happy holiday bus is here.
Now hurry or we'll be late.
Quick, pick up your tickets right over there.
We'll leave when the clock strikes eight.

The happy holiday bus consists of a row of chairs placed like seats on a bus. There are only enough seats for half of the children. The children stand outside of the bus to start the game.

Each child's name is written on a piece of paper; this is his ticket. The leader holds all of these tickets to the happy holiday bus. The leader then takes all of the tickets and spreads them out over the top of a table some distance away. This table represents the ticket office.

Everyone recites the verse above. Then they dash to the table to find their own correct ticket and quickly back to the leader who is standing by the bus. If a child has the right ticket with his own name on it, he may sit inside the happy holiday bus; if not, he must try again after returning the wrong ticket. As soon as the bus is filled with children, everyone says *"gong"* eight times for eight o'clock. The happy holiday bus must leave. The children pretend to create movement of the happy holiday bus by bouncing up and down and saying *"Beep, beep."* The others wave good-bye.

69

FUZZY LITTLE MONKEY

Fuzzy little monkey.
You can't come home with me.
I'll give you to my friend here,
Absolutely free.

The children sit in a circle and all speak the verse above. One child stands and holds the monkey (use a ball, sweater, or a bean bag to represent the monkey). The child holding the monkey is not allowed to take it home, so he must give it away. The child drops the monkey in the lap of another child.

The idea of the game is that no one may keep the monkey. So whoever receives the monkey, immediately drops it in the lap of another child.

Whoever is caught holding the monkey when the verse is completed each time gets a make-believe spanking for bringing the monkey home.

A LONELY LITTLE GHOST

A lonely little ghost would
Love some company.
He wants to have a ghost friend.
His ghost friend won't be me.

One child is chosen to be the lonely little ghost. He sits on a chair in the haunted house. Indicate a certain area for that purpose. The other children speak the verse and sneak into the haunted house. They tease the ghost. Any child he catches or tags within the boundaries of his haunted house becomes a ghost and joins him to try to catch the remaining children, who return again and again to tease and try to avoid being caught by the ghosts. The last child caught is the winner and may be the lonely little ghost the next time the game is played.

The WITCH'S MAGIC THIMBLE

Steal it quickly, snitchity snitch.
The magic thimble of the witch.
If you don't steal it while you are able,
The witch will put you under the table.

One child is chosen to be the witch. She sits in a chair, and puts her head on one end of the table, pretending to be asleep. One child at a time tries to steal her magic thimble. The magic thimble is placed on the table in a position that gives the witch an even chance to catch the child trying to steal it. The child, too, must have an even chance of getting away to the safety of the forest. Choose an area to represent the forest.

If the witch should catch the child before he is safe, the child is her prisoner and must sit under the table. If the child is not caught by the witch, he becomes the new witch and places the thimble back on the table. Now the game is repeated as before. The witch may stay a witch as long as she catches children to sit under her table. The winner is the witch who captures the most children.

This game is played in two parts.

Part 1

Open the gate, let the children come in.
Make-Believe Land is about to begin.
Find a small space, and hurry right through.
Wonderful things will be waiting for you.

This game is to be played with two teams. One team locks arms while standing in a row to form the gate to Make-Believe Land. The other team will try to break through the gate, sending one or two children at a time. The verse is recited one or more times, depending on the number of children playing the game. When the game is completed, count the number of children who have slipped through the gate. The children then change places, with the first gate-children trying to slip through the barrier made by the children who tried to slip through in the first game.

74

Part 2

The team with the most children having escaped through the gate to Make-Believe Land wins the game. They dance in a circle, chanting the second verse listed below, while the others clap hands and watch.

Let's dance in a circle, oh, one, two, and three.

Make-Believe Land is not just for me.

Come join in the fun, as we call all your names.

The gate is wide open to make-believe games.

The dancing winners call one member of the losing team at a time. Each child whose name is called walks over to join the dancing circle. When all have been called, the entire group march to their chairs. The chairs represent Make-Believe Land.

Swimming through the ocean blue,
A little school of fish.
A big fish wants to eat you.
Shoo fish, swish, swish, swish.

Choose one child to be the big fish. Ten or fewer children at one time, standing in a long row, represent a school of fish. The school of fish are swimming through the place where the big fish lives. The school of fish walk through the big fish's territory, each with his hands on the shoulders of the child in front of him. They are pretending to be big fish, too, by swimming close together. The last child in the line is the fish's tail.

The child chosen to be the big fish tries to capture the school of fishes' tail. The little school of fish try to protect their tail and get home safely before they are caught. If the big fish can pull the school of fishes' tail away before they are safely home, he becomes the new tail, and another child is chosen to play the big fish. The game should be repeated often enough so that each child gets a chance to be the big fish.

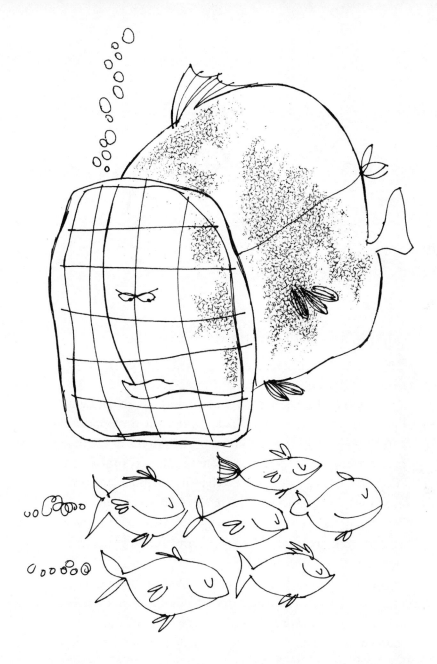

Here kitty, kitty, come home to me.
Be careful of (autos or doggies) that you see.

The children, on their hands and knees, pretend that they are kittens. The leader stands at the opposite end of the room from the kittens. The kittens crawl in a race toward the leader, but whenever she says the word "doggies" instead of "autos," the kittens must stop and arch their backs and say *"pssst,"* like an angry cat.

Then they continue to crawl as before. Whoever fails to stop on the word "doggies" and arch his back and say *"psst,"* is out of the game.

The verse is repeated over and over until the kittens reach their goal. The leader tries to fool the children by slipping in the word "doggies" often to eliminate as many as possible. The child who reaches the leader or the established goal first, with no mistakes, is the winner.

78

TAKE CARE OF MY LITTLE DOG, PLEASE

Take care of my little dog, please.
I must go away.
Oh, he'll be very good, you'll see,
If (name of a child) **can make him stay.**

One child is chosen to be the little dog. Another child is chosen to be the dog's master. The other children stand in a row with their hands on top of their heads. Each child represents a little house, their arms and hands represent the rooftops.

The master and his dog walk from their little house (which may be any designated spot) across the room to the row of houses. The dog's master speaks the verse and surprises the children by putting in one of their names (George, John, etc.). Then the child who has been named must chase the dog and try to catch him before the dog can run back home. If the child catches the dog, he may be the dog in the next game. If the dog is not caught, the game is repeated. A new master may be chosen for each new game.

FIRE CRACKERS

We're here to see the fireworks.
See the boom and the bang and the whee!
We hold our ears, then clap our hands,
For the whee, boom, bang we see.

Seat children on chairs in three different groups. Section one is the boom section, they represent the big firecrackers; section two is the bang section, they represent the little firecrackers; section three is the whee section, representing the rockets that go up.

80

This game may be played with three different variations.

1

All say the verse together repeatedly, using the speed best suited to the children playing. The boom or bang or whee sections stand separately, as their word is called. Only one section at a time stands.

2

The leader repeats the verse and mixes up the order of the words, making a contest of alertness to see which section is the most attentive and stands only on their word.

3

The leader repeats the verse and mixes up the words boom, bang, and whee, then whichever child makes a mistake in his section is disqualified and must leave the game. The game is repeated until one child remains as the winner.

WORK OR PLAY?

Mother speaks.

**"Come in, come in and stop your play.
The ones I catch must work today."**

Children speak.

**"Come in, come in and stop our play.
The ones you catch must work today."**

Choose a child to be the mother or father who must stand in one spot in the center of the circle. The others are the children. They hold hands and spread out into a large circle. As the children circle, the mother tags all she can reach without moving outside the small circle drawn for her to stand within.

Whoever she tags must get into her circle and help her tag the others. As the outside circle has fewer children, they may let go hands. The last one to be tagged becomes the new mother or father.

82

Statues in the Park

**I see bushes and trees and grass and
  flowers,**
Walking through the park.
People and birds and butterflies,
We'll walk and play till dark.

The children walk through a make-believe park.
They are listening as the leader speaks the above verse,
over and over. The leader will unexpectedly replace
one of the objects named with the word statues. Whoever does not freeze, but moves, is out of the game and
must sit on a make-believe park bench.

The game is repeated until all but one child is eliminated. The last child to freeze on command is the
winner. He may play the part of the leader in the next
game.

Ride 'em cowboy, watch us go.
Past the Indians to Mexico.

Start the game by choosing two children to be
Indians, standing in the center of the room. All of the
other children are cowboys on imaginary horseback.
The cowboys try to pass the Indians and ride safely to
Mexico. Only four cowboys at a time may try to run past
the two Indians. These four cowboys run together past
the Indians to reach a corner of the room which has been
designated as Mexico.

Whoever is tagged by an Indian before he reaches
Mexico must go as a prisoner and sit in the Indian
village, which is located in the opposite corner from
Mexico.

The entire game should be repeated numerous
times. Choose two new Indians for each new complete
game. The fun in this game is to see how many cowboys
can always escape the Indians and to see which pair of
Indians can capture the most cowboys.

We're climbing up a rainbow.
See the colors all aglow.
Up to the very top, heigh-ho!
We've had our turn, so down we go!

This game is played in a yard which has a children's slide. The children form a line, and the verse above is recited as they climb up to the top and slide down.

As each child reaches the bottom, he runs to the leader and must guess which color the top of the rainbow will be, red, yellow, or blue. The leader holds a crayon of one of these three colors in her hand. The children who guess which one of the three colors she is holding may line up for another turn climbing the new rainbow. The others are eliminated from the game.

The leader changes the colors with each repetition of the game, and the last child to guess correctly wins the game.

The WIND

The wind in the night goes *wooooooo*.
The owl in the tree says *whooooooo*.
My kitty looks up from her pillow of
**   blueoooooo.**
"I think they are speaking to youoooooo."

Choose one child to be the wind, and another child to be the kitty. The other children pretend to be in their beds listening to the wind outside saying *wooooooooo*. Children recite the first three lines of the verse.

The wind comes through an imaginary window to blow on the children. The kitty speaks the last line, "I think they are speaking to youoooooo." The kitty chooses a child who must chase the wind out of the window. If the wind is caught, the child who chases him may have a turn playing the part of the wind in the next game.

Where did the little blue airplane go?
High in the sky or down below?
We searched up and down and 'round and
   'round.
He must be hiding on the ground.

All of the children are little airplanes in this hide-and-seek game. One child hides himself or a toy airplane. Either the child or the model plane represents the lost airplane.

The other little airplanes are played by children with arms stretched out and standing on their toes—for they are high in the air. They go to search for the little lost airplane. They recite the verse as they fly about.

Whoever is first to find the little lost airplane rescues him and guides him home. Then the rescuer may have a turn as the next little lost airplane.

MR FROG AND MR TURTLE

Said Mr. Frog to Mr. Turtle,
"We've come to swim and keep cool."
"Oh, no you can't," the turtle said.
"It's only a turtle pool."

Play this game with two teams. One team made up of frogs and the other team of turtles. The two teams face each other. The Mr. Frog team speaks the first two lines. The Mr. Turtle team speaks the last two. Then immediately the frog team tries to pass the turtle team to a specified area representing the pool. If all of the frogs can pass the turtles in the amount of time allowed, the frogs are the winners of the pool.

Next time the game is played, let the turtles try to win back the pool from the frogs.

REDBiRDS, BLUEBiRDS

This wonderful rope will make a new nest,
In a beautiful apple tree.

Redbirds and bluebirds peeping aloud,
"Those apples are waiting for me, for me,
    for me."

90

Prepare an equal number of small red and small blue construction paper squares, so that each child playing receives one of each color. The children should be divided into two teams, the redbirds and the bluebirds.

The leader or an extra child may have the fun of tossing all the red and blue squares into the air. The squares represent flying red and bluebirds.

The children immediately grab one square apiece. All of those with red squares are the redbirds, and all of those with blue squares are the bluebirds. Each team wants to build a nest in the beautiful apple tree (any object may represent the tree).

The teams pick up opposite ends of a big rope. They say the verse together, then on the words "for me," they start a tug-of-war to see which team can pull the hardest and win the rope to build their nest. The winners make a circle of the rope, winding it around to represent a big nest. Then the winning team sits inside and says, "peep, peep, peep" like happy little birds.

WHO LET THE ANIMALS OUT OF THE ZOO ?

The children all sit in a row and make roars and growls as animals in the zoo. Then they stop and say the following verse.

What are the animals trying to say?
"They forgot to lock our cages today.
Let's run out and play, we can leave the zoo.
But what will the poor sleepy zoo keeper do?"

While the children are reciting the verse, the leader walks about and taps one child on the shoulder on the word "zoo keeper," and that child becomes the zoo keeper who must put his head down, close his eyes for a slow count to ten.

Now all of the other animals run and hide. After making his count to ten, the zoo keeper goes out to hunt for the animals. When he sees an animal, he must go within a couple of feet of him and call to him, and then the animal he sees must chase the zoo keeper; if the animal tags the keeper before he gets back to the zoo, the animal may escape into the countryside. If the animal gets all the way back to the zoo without tagging the zoo keeper, he is considered captured.

If a large group of children play, use two zoo keepers. The fun of the game is to see which zoo keeper can capture the most animals.

THE ZOO

I spin you around, in our zoo-catching game,

Then into your cage, and tell me your name.

Choose one child to be the zoo catcher. The zoo catcher whispers to the leader which kind of animal he wants to have sent to another zoo. The other children who play the part of any animal that they choose are not supposed to know which animal the zoo keeper plans to send away.

Now the game begins. The children all stand in a row facing the zoo keeper. One at a time, he grabs a child's hand and spins him around and says, "I spin you around in our zoo-catching game." Then the zoo catcher lets go and wherever the child lands will be his cage. The zoo catcher now says, "Then into your cage and tell me your name." The child tells whatever animal he is, and then must imitate that animal. The zoo catcher does the above with each child.

If there is a large group of children, two zoo catchers may be appointed. The leader must write down the names of all the children who represent the animal that the zoo catcher and the leader had previously and secretly planned to send away to another zoo. If the animal secretly chosen was a lion, all the lions must leave the game.

The remaining children line up as before. The leader then chooses a new zoo keeper by counting from the left of the row with the letters of the name of the animal that has been sent away. For example lion has four letters, so the fourth child would therefore become the new zoo keeper. The new zoo keeper secretly picks a new animal to be sent away, and he tells the leader, secretly, as before. The game is repeated until only one child remains as the winner. The leader may announce to the children four to six animals that they must choose to imitate, just before the game begins. This will simplify the game.

Let's Pretend We're Giants

**Let's pretend we're giants, in the
Land of little people.
We'll travel up the river, where we'll
Meet them by their steeple.**

The children pretend that they are giants in a land of little people. A long rope, such as a clothesline, is laid on the floor. It is called the Rope River. The children start at one end with their feet together. They must hop back and forth over the rope and pretend to be traveling up Rope River to the imaginary land of little people, who are waiting by their steeple. If the giants step on the rope or fall over it, they have landed in the Rope River and are out of the game. The winners reach the end of the rope safely and dry.

If the children are old enough for a variation, the game may be more fun if the rope is wiggled back and forth, creating a greater obstacle for hopping back and forth over the rough water of Rope River.

96

MY LION'S IN A RAGE

My lion's in a terrible rage.
He'll break right out of his iron cage.
Look out, look out, he's running through!
He just missed me, but he might catch you.
   Grrrrrrrrr!

In this game, the lion is a big ball such as a beach ball. The children form a circle around the ball. One child starts to roll the lion back and forth from child to child. The ball may roll in any direction as long as it remains in the circle.

The child closest to the ball must always push it away. Each child tries to avoid touching the ball. The above verse is recited as the children roll the ball about. When the verse is completed, and the sound *grrrrrrrrr* is made, whoever is caught with the ball is out of the game because the lion has caught him.

The game is repeated, and each time the circle will grow smaller as the lion catches someone in each game. The last child to be caught with the ball is the winner.

Let's ride our merry, merry-go-round.
Our horses go up, our horses go down.
Happy children, everyone sing.
Who will catch the shiny brass ring?

The children form a circle with their backs to the center. Now they are make-believe merry-go-round horses.

Choose one child to step out of the circle and stand in a stationary spot at the side. This child holds out a shiny ring, dangling from a ribbon, just barely within reach of the merry-go-round horses. Now the merry-go-round horses start to walk in a circle, moving up and down as merry-go-round horses move.

Everyone keeps repeating the verse, and each time they come to the word "ring," the children closest to the ring try to grab it. They cannot leave their positions on the merry-go-round. Whoever grabs the ring first wins a chance to hold the ring for the next game.

I'm a big ferocious dragon,
But bigger I want to grow.
This village has my dinner, sooooo,
It's you I'll eat, ho, ho!

One child plays the part of the dragon, who wants to grow bigger and bigger by eating more and more. The other children stand in a circle to represent the village. They place their hands, palms together, to represent peaked roof tops. The children pretend to hide in their huts.

The dragon goes to the village in search of food. He speaks the verse, and wherever and whenever he chooses to stop he grabs a child by surprise. The chosen child must hang onto the dragon's back, and he now becomes a part of the dragon. The dragon continues around the circle, repeating the verse.

If a large number of children play the game, the dragon may grab two at one time. The last child left in the village becomes the new dragon. All of the other children who have been captured become a part of the dragon.

101

TEDDY BEAR

Who is hiding behind the chair?
Peekaboo!
Who will take his teddy bear?
Little Loo!

102

Choose one child to sit in a chair and close his eyes. He is called Peekaboo. Place a teddy bear on the floor behind Peekaboo's chair. Choose another child to be Little Loo. The other children all sit in their chairs a short distance behind Peekaboo's chair. They all recite the verse.

Little Loo tries to take the teddy bear without Peekaboo guessing when he takes it. Whenever Peekaboo guesses that a child has picked it up and is holding the teddy bear, he looks around and says, "peekaboo." If Peekaboo catches him holding the teddy bear, he has another chance to play Peekaboo. The game is repeated, but a new Little Loo is chosen for the game to take the teddy bear. However, if Peekaboo turns around and says, "peekaboo," and the teddy bear has not been picked up, he is out of the game.

Then Little Loo starts the game again as Peekaboo and sits in his chair and guesses, while a new child is chosen to be the next Little Loo who tries to take the teddy bear.

Little Loo is safe, however, if after taking the teddy bear he can reach his chair undiscovered by Peekaboo. If safe, then he may also have a chance now to start a new game and be the new Peekaboo sitting in the chair and a new Little Loo is chosen.

Toot, toot, toot,
A beet, a bit, a boot.

The children all sit in a row facing the leader who speaks the verse over and over. He repeats the verse to both a quick and a slow tempo as the children act it out.

The children put their hands to their lips to blow imaginary horns for the words, "Toot, toot, toot."

They place their hands on their heads for the word, "beet." For the word, "bit," they put their hands in their laps. The children tap their shoes on the word, "boot."

The leader may demonstrate once for the children to show them how the motions are performed to the verse. But when the game starts, only the children make the motions with both hands. Only the leader recites the verse. The children will be too busy moving their hands from mouth, to head, to lap, to shoes to recite the verse. This game is just for fun and lively action. There are no winners.

104

I've come to buy a jack-in-the-box.
Which one will it be?
Pop up, go down, pop up, go down.
The best one is for me.

The children are sitting in a row or they may stoop
down. They represent jack-in-the-box toys in a toy shop.
One child is chosen to enter the shop to buy the best
jack-in-the-box in the shop.

To test which child is the best toy, the child enter-
ing the toy shop stops before a jack-in-the-box and
recites the verse above. He mixes up the third line any-
way he likes in order to confuse the jack-in-the-box.

He may say, "Pop up, pop up, go down, pop up," or
any combination that he wishes to use. He keeps repeating the verse with variations until the last child left is
the best jack-in-the-box and wins the game.

Who's There?

Our house has a bell, a bell with a *bong*.
The bell on the door, goes *bing, bong, bong*.

> The children remain seated, but tap their feet up
> and down on the floor. They are pretending to run
> to answer the door.

We run to the door, and we are aware,
Someone awaits, we ask, "Who's there?"

One child is chosen to ring the imaginary doorbell as he stands outside the house. All of the other children sit on chairs facing the child who rings the doorbell. They are all inside of the house and they recite the verse. After they say, "Who is there?" the child at the door must act out who is there without speaking.

For example he may be a father, a mother, a grandparent, a postman, an ice cream man, a playmate, a laundryman, a milkman or whoever the child at the door wishes to be. The first child to guess correctly wins and exchanges places with the child at the door.

The game may be played again, with a new child ringing the doorbell each time the identity of the former doorbell ringer is guessed. The game is played in an ordinary playroom or classroom. The door and the house are, of course, imaginary.

Go Duck, Go!

The great big pond is just the place,
Our quack, quack ducks will have a race.
So down in the water, and don't be slow,
Our quack, quack ducks are ready to go.

Each child is given a paper napkin which he crumples into a ball. This ball represents the duck's body. The child then pulls out a small piece of the paper ball and twists it to represent the protruding neck and head of a duck.

Then all the children take their paper-napkin ducks to a starting line for a race. Together, they speak the above verse. On the word "go," the children, on their hands and knees, take a big breath and blow their ducks along the floor toward an established finish line. Each child blows his individual duck as hard and as fast as he can, in order to make his duck come in first and win the race.

BUMPITY, BUMPITY

We begin the race with a *bumpity* song,
Bumpity, bumpity, bumping along.

This is a sitting-down race. All of the children line
up for a bumpy race. They sit in a long row facing a goal
on the other side of the room. They recite the first line of
the verse, and on the word *"bumpity,"* they start bumping along in their sitting positions to the goal across the
room. They keep repeating, *"bumpity, bumpity,* bumping along," until they reach the goal. The first one who
reaches the goal line wins the race.

109

LAUGH LITTLE CLOWN

Turn around little (girl or boy) **and make a funny face.**
If you make me laugh, then you may take my place.

Choose one child to be the clown for this game. He sits sadly on a chair. The remaining children sit in a row on chairs facing the clown, who tries not to smile.

The clown recites the verse as each child (one at a time) comes up to greet the clown. The child approaching the clown turns around just once and tries to make a funny face to make the clown smile right away. If he is not successful, he returns to his seat and the next child tries to make the clown smile. The game is repeated, and whenever a child does make the clown smile, the clown must change places with the youngster who made him smile.

Now the new clown tries not to smile as the children make their efforts. The game continues until all of the children have had a turn trying to make the clown smile. Each child, of course, hopes to be one of the new clowns.

#9063